Reader's Theater
Bible-Based
DRAMAS
new Testament

By
Connie Walters

Cover illustration by
Donna Perrone

Inside illustrations by
John Carrozza

Publisher
In Celebration™
A division of Instructional Fair • TS Denison
Grand Rapids, Michigan 49544

In Celebration™ Copyright Notice

Dedication

This book is dedicated to my sisters
Suzanne and Denise.
Thank you for all the love, prayers, and support
throughout the years.

Acknowledgments

My heartfelt gratitude to the following angels for their proofreading, feedback, and support: Denise O'Leary, Gail Ketola, Patty Van Ingen, Diane Totten, Clair Nofs, Molly McDonough, Gina Patrick, Jasmine and Brendan Kee.
My deepest appreciation to my husband, Herm Walters,
for his help, support, and patience and to my children and grandchildren, who were the inspiration for many of the characters in these stories.

Credits:
Author: Connie Walters
Cover Artist: Donna Perrone
Inside Illustrations: John Carrozza
Inside Border: Julie Anderson
Project Director/Editor: Alyson Kieda
Editors: Ruth Gray, Linda Triemstra
Graphic Layout: Deborah Hanson McNiff

About the Author:
Connie Walters has dedicated her talents to early childhood education for over 25 years. She has a degree in child development from Madonna University in Michigan. She cofounded the Novi Co-Op Nursery School and developed Loving Learning, a private preschool program. Ms. Walters is a composer, lyricist, and author of several books. Her husband, five children, three stepchildren, and six grandchildren continue to inspire and encourage her work.

Standard Book Number: 1-56822-699-3
Reader's Theater: Bible Based Dramas—New Testament
Copyright © 1998 by In Celebration™
A Division of Instructional Fair • TS Denison
2400 Turner Avenue NW
Grand Rapids, Michigan 49544

All Rights Reserved • Printed in the USA

Reader's Theater
Bible-Based Dramas
New Testament

Santa Tells the Story of Jesus

Narrators
Readers 1, 2, 3

Characters
Santa Claus
Gabriel, messenger angel from God
Mary, mother of Jesus
Joseph, spouse of Mary
Woodland animals:
    squirrel
    rabbit
    bear
    moose
Innkeepers 1, 2, 3
angels
shepherds
lambs
cow
donkey
children's choir

Costumes
traditional outfit
simple white tunic
light blue tunic
brown tunic
Costumes or animal head pieces may be sewn
or an enlargement of a picture of each animal
may be colored, cut out, and worn around the
child's neck by attaching yarn through holes
punched in the top of the mounted picture.
simple tunics
white tunics
dark tunics
head piece or picture
head piece or picture
head piece or picture

Props
Woodland scene:
    trees
    artificial snow
    tree stump
    woodland animals (stuffed toys, cardboard cutouts)
Stable scene:
    manger
    baby doll wrapped in white cloth

Lighting
spotlight

Backdrop
royal blue curtain

Setting
The stage area is divided into two scenes: a woodland scene on stage right and a stable scene
on stage left. (See diagram on page 6.)

Production Notes: This production offers many young children the opportunity to participate in the Christmas story as shepherds, angels, and animals. The script is written for actors to enter stage right or stage left. If the play is performed on the audience level rather than on a stage, consider the following alternative which enables the children to view the performance as well as partake in it.

Seat the SHEPHERDS in the audience in the first row on the left.
Seat the SHEEP in the second row in the audience on the left.
Seat the ANGELS in the third row in the audience on the left.
Seat all ANIMALS in the first row in the audience on the right.
Seat GABRIEL, MARY, and JOSEPH in the second row on the right.

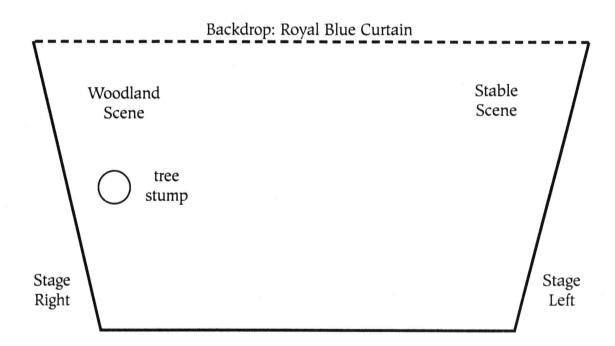

Backdrop: Royal Blue Curtain

Woodland Scene

Stable Scene

tree stump

Stage Right

Stage Left

Scene 1

Woodland scene—stage right
    Time: two weeks before Christmas
    Place: North Pole

Stable scene—stage left
    Time: the year of Jesus' birth
    Place: Bethlehem

*The song "Jingle Bells" by J. Pierpont is being played on the
piano accompanied by the sound of sleigh bells.
The READERS walk onto the apron area in front of stage area left.*

READER 1:   The story that you are about to hear happened just a few years ago, when Santa was busier than ever making toys to give to children on Christmas Eve. Children had asked for skateboards, rocket ships, and baby dolls that giggled and clapped their hands. *(Add the name of a toy that is currently popular.)*

READER 2:   On this busy afternoon, Santa decided to take a break. A long walk in the woods for some fresh air *(slight pause)* and some peace and quiet sounded great. Santa put down his hammer and took off his tool apron. Then, without a word to anyone, he left the toy shop.

READER 3:   As Santa stepped outdoors, he saw that it was a beautiful winter day. The sun was shining, the snow was sparkling, and the air was crisp. It was a perfect day for choosing the longest trail in the woods for a nice afternoon walk. *(SANTA enters from behind the audience shaking bells.)*

SANTA: Ho-Ho-Ho! What a beautiful day!
(SANTA slowly walks up from the back to the front of the audience as the three narrators read.)

READER 1:   It was gorgeous outside. Santa walked and walked for a long time. Now and then, he would stop to look at the evergreen trees. He knew that Mrs. Claus would soon ask him to choose their Christmas tree. *(SANTA stops.)*

SANTA: Now here's a beautiful tree!
(SANTA looks up and down an imaginary tree.)
I think Mrs. Claus would like this one. Wait a minute . . . maybe that one over there.
(SANTA points to another imaginary tree.)

READER 2: Santa continued on his walk, stopping a number of times to listen to the birds, watch the reindeer, and feed the squirrels. He was enjoying himself so much that he completely forgot about the time.

READER 3: It was getting late, and Santa was very tired. He sat down to rest his legs before heading back to the toy shop.
(SANTA has reached the woodland scene on stage right. He sits down on the ground and leans against the tree stump.)

SANTA: *(SANTA stretches his arms.)*
This has been such a wonderful walk. It is so beautiful out here.
(SANTA yawns.)

READER 1: It was very peaceful in the woods. Santa closed his eyes and took a deep breath. Soon, he was fast asleep.
(SANTA's chin drops to his chest as he snores loudly.)

READER 2: Santa slept for a long time. The sun had gone down, and it was getting dark. The animals had stopped playing. Most of them were heading back to their homes in the woods.
(SQUIRREL, RABBIT, BEAR, MOOSE enter on the right.)

READER 3: A few animals noticed Santa leaning against the tree stump in a deep sleep.
(SANTA snores loudly.)
The animals began chattering among themselves.

SQUIRREL: Ch, ch, ch! What's Santa doing here?

RABBIT: Why isn't he at his workshop making toys?

BEAR: How will he ever get the toys made on time for Christmas?

MOOSE: Maybe there won't be a Christmas this year!

SQUIRREL: No Christmas at all?

READER 1: The animals were getting quite noisy. Soon, all their chattering and chirping woke Santa!

SANTA: *(SANTA rubs his eyes and yawns.)*
What's happening here? What's going on?

SQUIRREL: Ch, ch, ch! Santa, what are you doing here?

RABBIT: Shouldn't you be at your workshop making toys?

BEAR: Are you gonna have all the toys ready for Christmas?

MOOSE: *(frustrated)* There'll be no Christmas this year. I just know it!

SANTA: No Christmas! Ho, ho, ho!
(SANTA stands.)
Of course there will be a Christmas! There will always be a Christmas! I'm not what Christmas is all about!

SQUIRREL: What do you mean, Santa?

SANTA: *(Beckons to the ANIMALS.)*
Come here, everyone. Let me explain what Christmas is all about. I'll tell you the story of the very first Christmas.

RABBIT: That's a great idea!
(SANTA steps forward on the stage. ANIMALS sit down near SANTA. READERS 1, 2, and 3 also sit down near SANTA to listen to the story.)

SANTA: Long ago, in the town of Nazareth, in the northern province of Galilee, there lived a young woman named Mary who loved God very much.
(MARY enters on stage left.)
One day as she was kneeling in prayer, a bright light appeared.
(MARY kneels with her hands folded in prayer as a bright light shines on her.)
There, standing before her, was an angel.

GABRIEL: *(GABRIEL enters stage left and walks into the light.)*
Don't be afraid, Mary. I am Gabriel, a messenger from God. God has chosen you to be the mother of his son.

MARY: I will do what God wants. May God's will be done.
(MARY bows her head.)

SANTA: Now in that same town, there lived a man named Joseph who loved Mary and wanted her to be his wife.
(JOSEPH enters stage left.)
One night when Joseph was sleeping, the angel Gabriel came to him in a dream.

GABRIEL: *(GABRIEL turns to JOSEPH.)*
Joseph, God has picked Mary to be the mother of his son. His name will be Jesus. God wants you to take care of Mary and Jesus.

JOSEPH: I will do what God wants of me.
(JOSEPH bows his head. GABRIEL leaves the stage.)

SANTA: Shortly after that, Joseph and Mary were married.
(MARY stands.)
One day, Joseph came home with some news to tell her.

JOSEPH: *(Facing MARY.)*
Mary, the emperor has ordered everyone to go to their hometown to pay taxes. He is taking a count of every person in the empire. I must go to Bethlehem in Judea. Perhaps you should stay here and wait for the baby to be born.

MARY: I want to go with you, Joseph. God will take care of us.

JOSEPH: *(Nods his head.)*
Yes, Mary, God will take care of us.

SANTA: The trip to Bethlehem was long.
(JOSEPH and MARY walk on an imaginary path.)
The road was very rough. The cold winds blew hard. Joseph and Mary were tired, but at last they arrived in Bethlehem.
(JOSEPH and MARY stand stage center.)

MARY: *(concerned)* Joseph, I hope we can find a room at the inn. It's almost time for the baby to be born.

SANTA: The streets were very crowded with people who had come to register. Mary and Joseph could not find a place to stay.

INNKEEPER 1: *(Enters stage left.)*
The inn is full. Try down the street.
(Exits stage right.)

INNKEEPER 2: *(Enters stage left.)*
Sorry, no vacancies. You cannot stay here.
(Exits stage right.)

SANTA: Now, there was a stable in the back of an inn where animals were kept.
(The COW and the DONKEY enter stage left and walk to the stable.)
It was here that a kind innkeeper offered Joseph and Mary a place to rest.

INNKEEPER 3: *(Enters stage left.)*
I can't give you a room. The inn is overcrowded. But I do have a stable in the back. You're welcome to stay there.

JOSEPH: Thank you, kind sir.
(JOSEPH smiles at the INNKEEPER, who then exits stage right.)

SANTA: Joseph and Mary went to the stable, where the baby was born that very night.
(JOSEPH and MARY walk over to the stable. MARY picks up the doll which is hidden there.)

MARY: *(Wraps the white cloth tightly around the doll.)*
Oh, Joseph, the baby is beautiful. God has been so good to us. He has answered the prayers of our people.

JOSEPH: Yes, Mary. He has sent us a savior, Jesus.
(MARY places the baby in the manger.)

SANTA: It was that night, the first Christmas so many years ago, that Mary gave birth to God's son, Jesus, the promised Savior. Jesus came to bring love and peace to the world.
(SANTA kneels and bows his head during a moment of silence.)
(CHOIR sings one verse of "Silent Night.")

Silent Night
Silent night! Holy night!
All is calm, all is bright,
Round yon Virgin, Mother and Child.
Holy Infant, so tender and mild,
Sleep in heavenly peace,
Sleep in heavenly peace.

SANTA: *(SANTA stands.)* On that same night, many shepherds were in the fields watching their sheep.
(SHEPHERDS enter stage left and walk to center stage.)
(SHEEP enter stage left and sit on the floor making "baa" sounds.)

Suddenly, there was a bright light in the sky.
(Spotlight shines in the center of the stage area.)
An angel sent by God appeared to the shepherds.

GABRIEL: *(Enters stage left and faces the SHEPHERDS.)*
Don't be afraid. I bring good news! Today, a Savior has been born. He is the savior of the world.

SANTA: The angels came from everywhere filling the sky.
(ANGELS enter stage left. As they do, the CHILDREN'S CHOIR sings "Angels We Have Heard on High"; the ANGELS join in the singing at the refrain.)

Angels We Have Heard on High
Angels we have heard on high
Sweetly singing o'er the plains,
And the mountains in reply
Echo back their joyous strains.

(refrain)
Glo-oooo-oooo-o-oooo-oria in excelsis Deo.
Glo-oooo-oooo-o-oooo-oria in excelsis Deo.

SANTA: *(SANTA steps forward and faces the audience.)*
And so, my friends, this is what Christmas is all about.
(SANTA extends his hand to the stable scene.)
God loves us so much that he sent his son, Jesus, to show us how to love one another. This is why I bring gifts on Christmas Eve. It's my way of showing love to everyone.
(Gestures with both hands to entire audience.)
This is what Christmas is all about—everyone giving gifts of love to one another just as God gave us Jesus, his gift of love, on that first Christmas night so very long ago.

ALL: *(sing refrain from "Angels We Have Heard on High")*

Glo-oooo-oooo-o-oooo-oria in excelsis Deo.
Glo-oooo-oooo-o-oooo-oria in excelsis Deo.

The Playful Angel

Characters	Costumes
Mary, mother of Jesus	pastel tunic
Joseph, Mary's husband	pastel tunic
Elizabeth, Mary's cousin	pastel tunic
Gloria, angel who announces Jesus' birth	white gown* with gold sash plus wings
Shepherds 1, 2, 3, 4	dark robes or tunics; headdress can be towel or material held in place with ribbon, cloth, or rope; walking sticks
Narrator Angel	simple white gowns,* each with a different colored sash plus angel wings
Michael, the archangel	
Gabriel, messenger of God	
Lucinda, supervises the dancing angels	
Dancing Angels 　Alexandria, the playful angel 　Thomas, Alexandria's playmate 　Jonathan 　Celeste 　Christine 　Angela	light pastel gowns,* no wings until: 　Scene 5 for Celeste, Jonathan, Thomas 　Scene 7 for Christine, Angela, 　　Alexandria

Choir Angels
　4–6 singing angels with wings
　keyboard angel who plays the keyboard (piano or synthesizer)

* Angels' gowns can be made of sheets, curtains, tablecloths, or any flowing material.

Props
scroll or book with script for the Narrator angel
bouncing ball for Alexandria
bench for the angels to sit on in heaven
baby doll
receiving blanket (white) to wrap baby Jesus
receiving blanket (light color) for Mary to cover baby Jesus
manger for baby Jesus
6 gold stars for Michael to pin on gowns of little dancing angels
small red heart with elastic for Alexandria to wear on her wrist

Lighting
spotlight

Setting
The stage area is set up as heaven and earth. The backdrop for heaven can be a light blue cloth or curtain across the entire width of the back of the stage area, with a few white felt clouds attached. Earth is set up in the front area of stage right. The backdrop for earth can be a royal blue cloth about six feet wide, draped over a room divider or standing chalk board. In a smaller area, a large plant can be placed in the front stage right area to symbolize earth.

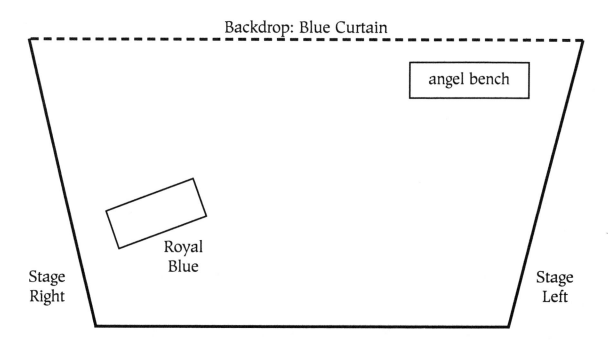

Scene 1—Heaven

THOMAS, JONATHAN, CELESTE, CHRISTINE, and ANGELA
are swaying and twirling to the song "The Six Dancing Angels."
This can be played by the angel at the keyboard (see page 17).

LUCINDA: *(Enters and claps her hands twice.)*
Are we ready to practice our dance for God, little angels?
(LITTLE ANGELS smile and nod their heads.)

CELESTE: I am.

THOMAS: I am.

JONATHAN: I am too!

CHRISTINE AND ANGELA:
Us, too.

LUCINDA: Let the music begin.
(LUCINDA looks at the KEYBOARD ANGEL, who plays a brief introduction to the song "The Six Dancing Angels.")

THOMAS: Wait! Where is Alexandria? Alexandria's not here!

LUCINDA: Oh, dear! Let me see! Have I forgotten to take roll call?
(The LITTLE ANGELS giggle.)
Where's my list? Oh, here it is!
(She walks toward the bench, picks up the list, and begins to read. Each ANGEL bows or curtsies as his or her name is read.)

Now then, Celeste, Christine, Angela, Jonathan, Thomas, and Alexandria.
Alexandria! *(pause)* Alexandria? Where are you?
(ALEXANDRIA comes running in, stage left, with a rubber ball in her hands.)

ALEXANDRIA: Here I am! I was playing ball with Moses.

LUCINDA: Alexandria, we were about to begin. You might have missed the dance practice.

ALEXANDRIA: *(Lowers her head with eyes down.)*
I'm sorry.

LUCINDA: *(Motions to ALEXANDRIA.)*
Quickly now, come and join us.
(ALEXANDRIA joins LUCINDA and the other angels. The music begins again.)

(CHOIR ANGELS sing.)
Oh, look high in the heavens there. *(three times)*
Angels are dancing for God.

See six little angels—they're spinning and twirling. *(three times)*
They're dancing before our God.

Oh, look high in the heavens there. *(three times)*
Angels are dancing for God.

See six little angels—they're sliding and gliding. *(three times)*
They're dancing before our God.

Oh, look high in the heavens there. *(three times)*
Angels are dancing for God.

See six little angels—they're rocking and swaying. *(three times)*
They're dancing before our God.

MICHAEL:	*(Enters stage right and claps at the end of the dance.)* That was beautiful, little angels. God will be so pleased. *(ALL ANGELS gather around MICHAEL.)*
JONATHAN:	Thank you, Michael.
CELESTE:	Yes, thank you.
CHRISTINE:	We're glad you liked it!
MICHAEL:	I have some special news to tell all of you.
THOMAS:	What is it, Michael?
ANGELA:	Tell us, Michael.
ALEXANDRIA:	Yes, please tell us.
MICHAEL:	Soon a great miracle will take place on earth. Long ago, God promised to send a Savior to the world. The time is now. God is going to send his Son. He will be born in Bethlehem.
CHRISTINE:	That's great news, Michael!
JONATHAN:	It's wonderful!
MICHAEL:	Yes, it is. God's people have been waiting a long time for this to happen. God has chosen a special young woman in Nazareth. He is sending Gabriel to tell her that she will be the mother of his son.
CELESTE:	Oh, how exciting!
ANGELA:	What's her name?
MICHAEL:	Her name is Mary. *(ANGELS exit. ALEXANDRIA is the last to leave. She bounces her ball; it rolls. She chases after it and picks it up.)*
ALEXANDRIA:	Wait for me! I'm coming. *(Exits.)*

Scene 2—Earth

The KEYBOARD ANGEL plays the first two lines of "Lo, How a Rose E're Blooming." The spotlight shines on the royal blue curtain. The NARRATOR ANGEL enters stage right, stands in front of the royal blue curtain, and unrolls the scroll. GABRIEL and MARY now enter stage right in front of the curtain. MARY kneels sideways, facing GABRIEL, with hands folded in prayer.

NARRATOR ANGEL:
God sent the angel Gabriel to the city of Galilee in Nazareth with a message for a young woman named Mary, who was engaged to Joseph from the family of King David.

GABRIEL:
Do not be afraid, Mary. God has chosen you to have a son. He will be great and will be called the Son of the Highest. His name is to be Jesus.

MARY:
May God's will be done!
(Bows her head. The spotlight fades.)
(The KEYBOARD ANGEL plays the remaining lines of the song.)

Scene 3—Heaven

ALEXANDRIA and THOMAS are playing a hand-clapping game at stage center.

Hand-Clapping Game
Melody: This Ol' Man

Come with me; you will be
Very happy, yes indeed.
Here in heaven, you will see
Angels dance and sing.
Come and play before the King.

GABRIEL:
(Enters stage left.)
That looks like fun!

ALEXANDRIA:
It's a new hand-clapping game. I wrote the words for Abraham. Do you think he'll like it, Gabriel?

GABRIEL:
I'm sure that he will. You certainly like to dance and sing and play games, don't you, Alexandria?

ALEXANDRIA:	*(Giggles.)* I really do. Tomorrow, I'm going to teach Noah a rainbow dance. I can hardly wait to teach baby Jesus some happy songs and games and dances.
THOMAS:	*(Smiles.)* You'll have to wait a little while, Alexandria.
GABRIEL:	Alexandria, you are the most cheerful and playful angel I've ever seen! *(Puts an arm around ALEXANDRIA.)*
ALEXANDRIA:	Thank you, Gabriel.
GABRIEL:	And you, Thomas . . . *(GABRIEL places the other arm around THOMAS.)* You are the best friend any angel could ever have. *(GABRIEL looks at ALEXANDRIA.)* Alexandria, you are blessed to have Thomas as your friend and playmate.
ALEXANDRIA:	I know, Gabriel. I sure am thankful. *(JONATHAN, CELESTE, and CHRISTINE enter stage right.)*
JONATHAN:	Look, Celeste. Gabriel is back.
CELESTE:	I see. Let's ask about Mary. *(ANGELS gather around GABRIEL.)* Did you visit Mary, Gabriel?
GABRIEL:	Yes, I did, Celeste.
JONATHAN:	Is she pretty?
GABRIEL:	*(Nods head affirmatively.)* She is very pretty. God's light shines brightly in her.
CHRISTINE:	Was she pleased, Gabriel?
CELESTE:	Tell us, please.
GABRIEL:	Yes my little ones. She was frightened but overjoyed at the news. She loves God very much. *(LITTLE ANGELS giggle and clap their hands with joy.)* Now I must go to Joseph and tell him about God's plan.

Scene 4—Earth

The KEYBOARD ANGEL plays the first verse of "What Child Is This?" The spotlight shines on the royal blue curtain. While the music plays, the NARRATOR ANGEL enters stage right, stands in front of the royal blue curtain, and unrolls the scroll. GABRIEL and JOSEPH enter stage right, in front of the curtain. They stand sideways, facing each other.

NARRATOR ANGEL:
Mary was engaged to Joseph, a descendant of King David's family. One night an angel from the Lord came to Joseph in a dream.

GABRIEL:
Joseph, son of David, do not be afraid. God wants you to take Mary as your wife. She will give birth to a son and you shall call him Jesus. He will save his people.

JOSEPH:
I will do God's will. *(Bows his head; the spotlight fades.)*
(THE KEYBOARD ANGEL plays the remaining lines of the song. ALL exit.)

Scene 5—Heaven

ALEXANDRIA, THOMAS, CELESTE, and JONATHAN are playing a circle game. ALEXANDRIA is the only angel without wings. Holding hands, the ANGELS go around in a circle while singing the song. At the end, they drop hands, raise their arms, and shout "Amen."

Circle Game
Melody: Ring Around the Rosie

Welcome to God's city.
Welcome to God's city.
Heaven, heaven
Shout "Amen!" *(shout)* Amen!

(ALEXANDRIA falls down as everyone shouts "Amen." MICHAEL enters quickly.)

MICHAEL:
Let me help you up!
(MICHAEL helps ALEXANDRIA to her feet.)
Alexandria, aren't you supposed to be helping polish those halos?

ALEXANDRIA:
Oh, dear. I forgot. I better go.
(ALEXANDRIA takes a few steps, stops, and turns to MICHAEL.)
Michael, can I ask you something?

MICHAEL:	What is it, Alexandria?
ALEXANDRIA:	Where will baby Jesus be born?
MICHAEL:	In Israel, in the little town of Bethlehem, five miles from Jerusalem.
ALEXANDRIA:	Michael, can I go to Bethlehem with the other angels to see baby Jesus?
MICHAEL:	Well, little one, it depends on if you have your wings by then. So, you better show what a good helper you are. Right?
ALEXANDRIA:	I will, Michael. I'll hurry. (*ALEXANDRIA skips off.*) (*CELESTE and CHRISTINE walk off behind her singing, "Welcome to God's city. Welcome to God's city. Heaven, heaven, shout 'Amen.'" THOMAS remains.*)
MICHAEL:	Thomas, I see that you have your wings. I'm very happy for you.
THOMAS:	Thank you, Michael. I'm happy too. I do hope that Alexandria will get her wings before baby Jesus is born.
MICHAEL:	So do I, Thomas. But she has to earn them just like you did. It seems to be taking her a bit longer. Perhaps you can remind her to do her good deeds.
THOMAS:	Okay! I will. (*THOMAS turns to walk off. He stops and turns to face MICHAEL.*) Michael, I wonder if Alexandria's games could be considered as good deeds. She has made up games and new songs and dances for Moses, Noah, King David, Gabriel, and so many of the angels. She makes everyone happy.
MICHAEL:	That's true, Thomas. She does take time to play with others and make them happy. I'll talk to someone about it.
THOMAS:	Oh, that's great! Thank you. By the way, Michael, I was thinking about Mary. What is Mary doing while she's waiting for baby Jesus to be born?
MICHAEL:	Mary has gone to visit her cousin Elizabeth, who is going to have a baby very soon. He will be known as John the Baptist. Now, let's go and put in a good word for Alexandria. (*THOMAS smiles and walks offstage left with MICHAEL as they both sing, "Come with me; you will be very happy, yes indeed. Here in heaven, you will see, angels dance and sing. Come and play before the King."*)

Scene 6—Earth

The KEYBOARD ANGEL *plays the first two lines of "It Came Upon the Midnight Clear." The spotlight shines on the royal blue curtain. While the music plays, the* NARRATOR ANGEL *enters stage right, stands in front of the royal blue curtain, and unrolls the scroll.* MARY *and* ELIZABETH *enter stage right and stand in front of the curtain facing each other.*

NARRATOR ANGEL:
When Elizabeth heard Mary's greeting, she spoke out with a loud voice.

ELIZABETH: Blessed are you, Mary, and blessed is the baby you will bear!

MARY: With all my soul, I praise the Lord. The almighty God has done great things for me. Holy is his name.
(Bows her head; the spotlight fades.)
(The KEYBOARD ANGEL *plays the remaining lines of the song.* ALL *exit.)*

Scene 7—Heaven

LUCINDA *directs the* CHOIR ANGELS *at center stage in the opening lines of "Hark! the Herald Angels Sing." At the front area of stage left,* MICHAEL *pins gold stars on* CHRISTINE *and* ANGELA'S *gowns.* CELESTE *and* JONATHAN *look on.* THOMAS *sits on the angels' bench.*

CHOIR ANGELS: *(singing)*

> Hark! the herald angels sing,
> "Glory to the newborn king"

LUCINDA: *(beaming)* Very good! Wonderful! Now let's sing it all the way through.

CHOIR ANGELS: *(singing)*

> **Hark! The Herald Angels Sing**
> Hark! the herald angels sing,
> "Glory to the newborn King;
> Peace on earth and mercy mild,
> God and sinners reconciled!"
> Joyful, all ye nations rise,
> Join the triumph of the skies;
> With the angelic hosts proclaim,
> "Christ is born in Bethlehem!"
> Hark! the herald angels sing,
> "Glory to the newborn King!"

(As the CHOIR ANGELS sing, CHRISTINE and ANGELA quietly admire their new wings as well as the gold stars that MICHAEL has just pinned on them. They exit stage left. MICHAEL pins stars on JONATHAN and CELESTE, who quietly admire each other's stars and exit stage left.)

(The CHOIR ANGELS finish singing. They look at LUCINDA for her reaction.)

LUCINDA: (beaming) That was beautiful! You've all done a wonderful job.
(CHOIR ANGELS smile.)
That's exactly the way we'll sing it! Let's go sing for Gabriel right now!
(LUCINDA and the CHOIR ANGELS exit stage right.)

THOMAS: (THOMAS stands up and walks over to MICHAEL, who pins a star on his robe.)
Where is Alexandria, Michael? I want to see how she looks with her wings.

MICHAEL: I think I see her coming, Thomas.

ALEXANDRIA: (Enters stage right, running.)
Michael! Oh, Michael! Look! I have wings. I'm a real angel now.
(Twirls around.)

MICHAEL: Yes, you certainly are, Alexandria. I am so happy you have your wings.
Now, let me give you a star.
(MICHAEL pins a gold star on ALEXANDRIA'S gown.)

THOMAS: (Smiles at ALEXANDRIA.)
Alexandria! You look beautiful! I have something for you.
(THOMAS looks at MICHAEL.)
Do I have time to give it to her, Michael?

MICHAEL: Yes, but don't take too long. Gabriel wants to see all the angels right away.

ALEXANDRIA: We'll hurry, Michael.

THOMAS: Yes, we'll be right there.

MICHAEL: Okay. See you there!
(MICHAEL exits stage right.)

ALEXANDRIA: (Walks over to THOMAS.)
Oh, Thomas! I just love my wings!
(Twirls.)

THOMAS: *(admiringly)* They look great on you, Alexandria! And here is a special heart from me to you.
(THOMAS hands ALEXANDRIA a small red heart attached to a circle of elastic to wear on her wrist.)

ALEXANDRIA: Oh, thank you, Thomas. You're a great friend. I'll keep it forever.
(ALEXANDRIA puts the red heart on her wrist.)

THOMAS: I'm glad you like it.

ALEXANDRIA: I do.
(ALEXANDRIA lifts her arm; the red heart dangles from her wrist.)
Thomas, I wonder if we can spin faster now that we have wings?

THOMAS: Let's try it.
(Taking ALEXANDRIA's hands, they spin faster and faster as they chant.)

THOMAS AND ALEXANDRIA:
(chant)
Angel, angel, do good deeds *(speak softly and spin slowly)*
Angel, angel, pick up speed *(pick up speed and volume)*
Angel, angel, go real fast! *(faster and louder)*
Angel, angel, wings at last! Hurray! *(stop and clap hands)*

ALEXANDRIA: That was so much fun. Let's do it one more time! Please!

THOMAS: Well . . . okay!

THOMAS AND ALEXANDRIA:
(chant)
Angel, angel, do good deeds *(speak softly and spin slowly)*
Angel, angel, pick up speed *(pick up speed and volume)*
Angel, angel, go real fast! *(faster and louder)*
Angel, angel, wings at last! Hurray! *(stop and clap hands)*

ALEXANDRIA: Oh, Thomas! My wings do help me spin faster. And now I can go with you and the other angels to tell the shepherds that Jesus is born.

ANGELS: *(Voices are singing in the background.)*
Glo-oooo-o-oooo-o-oooo-oria in excelsis Deo!

THOMAS: Do you hear that, Alexandria?

ALEXANDRIA: Oh, no! We're too late! Thomas, the angels are singing to the shepherds!

THOMAS: Come, Alexandria! Let's hurry to the fields and join them!

ANGELS: *(singing)* Glo-oooo-o-oooo-o-oooo-oria in excelsis Deo!

Scene 8—Earth

The KEYBOARD ANGEL *plays the first four lines of "The First Noel." The spotlight shines on the royal blue curtain. While the music plays, the* NARRATOR ANGEL *enters stage right, stands in front of the curtain, and unrolls the scroll.* GABRIEL *and* SHEPHERDS *enter stage right and stand sideways in front of the curtain with* GABRIEL *facing the* SHEPHERDS.

NARRATOR ANGEL:

Shepherds were in the fields keeping watch over their flock when suddenly an angel of the Lord appeared to them.

GLORIA: I bring you good news. This day, in the city of David, there is born to you a Savior, who is Christ the Lord.

SHEPHERDS: Let's go to Bethlehem and see the baby who is our Savior, Christ the Lord. *(The spotlight fades. The* KEYBOARD ANGEL *plays the song's refrain.* ALL *exit.)*

Scene 9—Heaven

GABRIEL *enters stage right reading a scroll as he walks toward center stage.*
ALEXANDRIA *and* THOMAS *enter stage right and walk toward* GABRIEL.

THOMAS: *(calls out)* Gabriel! Gabriel!

GABRIEL: *(Turns to* THOMAS *and* ALEXANDRIA.*)*
Hello, Thomas! Hello, Alexandria!

ALEXANDRIA: *(sniffles)* Oh, Gabriel! I feel so sad. Thomas and I wanted to sing to the shepherds, but we were too late.

THOMAS: We rushed to the spot where we heard the angels singing, but by the time we got there the shepherds and angels were gone.

ALEXANDRIA: *(sniffles)* It was all my fault. I asked Thomas to play with me. That's why we were late getting there.

GABRIEL:	(*lovingly*) Alexandria, I know that you are a very playful angel and sometimes you are not on time. But I also know that you make other angels happy. Now, dry your tears. I will tell you how to find baby Jesus. (*GABRIEL wipes ALEXANDRIA's tears with a tissue.*)
ALEXANDRIA:	Thank you, Gabriel.
GABRIEL:	You're welcome. Now, go with Thomas to Bethlehem and look for a great big star. It will be shining over the place where Jesus is lying in a manger.
THOMAS:	Thank you, Gabriel.
ALEXANDRIA:	Yes, thank you very much.
GABRIEL:	You're welcome. (*THOMAS and ALEXANDRIA exit stage right. GABRIEL exits stage left.*)

Scene 10—Earth

The spotlight shines on the royal blue curtain. MARY enters stage right with the baby in her arms. JOSEPH follows. They stand in front of the curtain. GABRIEL and MICHAEL carry the manger and put it near MARY and JOSEPH. Four SHEPHERDS enter stage left, walk over to stage right, and kneel sideways looking at MARY and her baby. LUCINDA, the CHOIR ANGELS, and the six DANCING ANGELS enter stage left where they stand to sing "The First Noel."

(The KEYBOARD ANGEL plays "The First Noel." The SHEPHERDS and all the ANGELS sing.)

SHEPHERDS AND ANGELS:
    (*singing*)

> **The First Noel**
> The first Noel, the angel did say
> Was to certain poor shepherds in fields as they lay
> In fields where they lay
> Keeping their sheep
> On a cold winter's night that was so deep
> Noel, noel, noel, noel
> Born is the king of Israel.

MARY:	Thank you, dear shepherds, for your beautiful song. I think that I heard heavenly angels singing with you.
JOSEPH:	We thank you for coming on this cold night.

SHEPHERD 1:   *(rises)* We are so happy to see baby Jesus.

SHEPHERD 2:   *(rises)* The angels told us where we could find him.
(The last two SHEPHERDS rise.)

SHEPHERD 3:   They told us that God sent him to be our Savior.

SHEPHERD 4:   We must go and tell others of this great happening.
(SHEPHERDS exit stage right. ANGELS exit stage left singing one verse of "Joy to the World" without keyboard accompaniment.)

ANGELS: *(singing)*

Joy to the World
Joy to the world,
The Lord is come!
Let earth receive her King;
Let e'vry heart prepare Him room
And heav'n and nature sing,
And heav'n and nature sing,
And heav'n, and heav'n and nature sing.

(All is quiet. MARY places the baby in the manger and covers the baby with the cloth that lies in the manger.)

JOSEPH: *(Facing MARY.)*
God has truly blessed us, Mary.

MARY: Yes, Joseph. Let us give God praise and thanksgiving.
(MARY and JOSEPH fold their hands, look lovingly at the baby Jesus in the manger, and bow their heads to pray.)
(ALEXANDRIA and THOMAS enter stage left. They walk over to the manger.)

THOMAS: *(Looks at the baby in the manger.)*
Oh, my! Look, Alexandria. Baby Jesus is so beautiful.

MARY: Joseph, I see two angels.

JOSEPH: I do too, Mary!

ALEXANDRIA: *(Looks at MARY and JOSEPH.)*
We came to see baby Jesus.

THOMAS: I hope that we didn't startle you. We've been so excited!

ALEXANDRIA: Can we do something special for baby Jesus? Can we dance for him?

MARY: That would be very special. I'm sure it will make him happy. *(She picks up the baby and holds him in her arms.)*

ALEXANDRIA: And when he gets bigger I'm going to teach him songs and play games with him!
(MARY and JOSEPH smile.)

JOSEPH: How wonderful! An angel to play with Jesus!
(The KEYBOARD ANGEL plays "Six Dancing Angels." [See page 17.])
(THOMAS and ALEXANDRIA dance to the music.)

(MICHAEL, GABRIEL, and the CHOIR ANGELS enter stage left at the back of the stage. They sing the lyrics found on page 17.)

(LUCINDA, CHRISTINE, ANGELA, JONATHAN, and CELESTE enter stage left and join THOMAS and ALEXANDRIA in the dancing.)

ALEXANDRIA: *(At the end of the dance, ALEXANDRIA looks toward baby Jesus and shouts:)* Happy Birthday, baby Jesus!

ALL: *(shouting)* Happy Birthday!

Cousin Jeremiah's Love for Jesus

Characters

Jeremiah, cousin of James and John, who lives in Jerusalem
Benjamin, Jeremiah's good friend, who lives in Bethany
*James, disciple of Jesus
*John, disciple of Jesus
*Peter, disciple of Jesus
Joshua, young boy living in Jerusalem
Miriam, Joshua's sister
Elizabeth, Joshua's youngest sister
Judith, Joshua's sister
Thaddeus, Joshua's brother
Jason, Joshua's brother
Martha, Jeremiah's mother
Lydia, Jeremiah's sister
Ann, Jeremiah's sister
Israelites 1, 2, 3, 4, 5, 6
*Jesus
*Mary Magdalene
Israelites to sing and act as crowd

*All characters are fictional except those marked with an asterisk.**

Props

tall, potted leafy plant or cardboard cutout of a tree
dreidl
marbles
palm branches and/or leafy branches
posterboard donkey with handles attached to the back
small table and tablecloth
bench or chair
3 bowls and 3 spoons
glass bottle for vinegar
bowl with covered lid
2 mats and 2 white sheets
outdoor bench
stringed instrument to represent a lyre

Costumes

All characters wear simple tunics. Jesus wears a white tunic and headdress.

Setting

Keep the setting simple by using a colored backdrop for the background and props to indicate the location of each scene. Prop people are needed to change props between scenes.

For Scenes 2, 3, 6, 7, and 10: one cardboard cutout tree on stage left to indicate that the scene takes place outdoors, in Jerusalem, or on the road to Jerusalem.

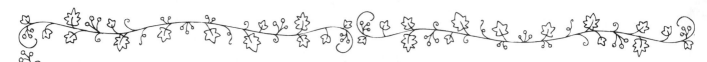

For Scenes 4, 5, and 8: one small table, a tablecloth, a bench or chair to indicate the scene takes place in Jeremiah's home.

For Scene 7: the leafy plant remains on stage left but in addition one outdoor bench is placed on stage right to indicate the outside of Jeremiah's home in Jerusalem.

Scene 1—Midafternoon in Bethany

BENJAMIN: *(Enters stage left, running.)*
Jeremiah! Jeremiah! Come quickly! Your cousins are coming! They're almost to the village!

JEREMIAH: *(Enters stage right.)*
Who is it, Benjamin? Who did you see?

BENJAMIN: *(BENJAMIN walks toward JEREMIAH.)*
Your cousins, James and John, the sons of Zebedee.

JEREMIAH: They must be on their way to Jerusalem for the Passover feast.

BENJAMIN: But why are they stopping here in Bethany?

JEREMIAH: I don't know. Come, Benjamin! Let's go meet them.
(BENJAMIN and JEREMIAH walk toward stage left.)
(JAMES and JOHN enter stage left.)

JEREMIAH: James! John!

JAMES: Well, if it isn't our cousin, Jeremiah, and his friend, Benjamin! Shalom, boys!

JOHN: Yes, peace be to both of you! What are you doing here in Bethany, Jeremiah?

JEREMIAH: I've been staying with Benjamin this past week. We've been helping his mother, Sarah, with some chores that need to be done before Passover.

JAMES: *(Staring at BENJAMIN.)*
Look how tall you are, Benjamin! You've really grown since the last time I saw you!

BENJAMIN: Well, it has been a couple of years since I've seen you, James. I hope that you and John can stay for supper.

JAMES:	I'm afraid we can't, Benjamin. Not today. We're on an errand.
JOHN:	Yes, and we have to get back quickly to our master.
JEREMIAH:	You mean Jesus? Is Jesus here in Bethany?
JOHN:	Jesus is nearby, Jeremiah. He's resting.
JEREMIAH:	*(excitedly)* Where? Tell me where he is, John! Please!
JOHN:	When we left him, he was near Bethphage on the Mount of Olives.
JEREMIAH:	I want to see him. Please take me to him.
JAMES:	We must first attend to our errand, Jeremiah. Jesus sent us to find a mother donkey with her young colt. Maybe you can help us.
BENJAMIN:	*(Steps towards JAMES.)* I can help you! This morning, I saw a donkey and her young one. They were tied up not far from here. *(BENJAMIN beckons with his hand.)* Come, I will show you.
JEREMIAH:	After your errand, will you be traveling to Jerusalem?
JAMES:	We'll join Jesus and the disciples and then head for Jerusalem.
JEREMIAH:	May I travel with you, please?
JAMES:	Are you ready to go now, Jeremiah?
JEREMIAH:	Yes! We finished all the chores this morning. *(Turns to BENJAMIN.)* Right, Benjamin?
BENJAMIN:	Yes, we've done all that we can do. *(Facing JEREMIAH.)* You've been a great help to us, Jeremiah, and I thank you.
JEREMIAH:	You're welcome, Benjamin. I'll come and help again, but now I have to get back home for Passover. *(Facing JAMES and JOHN.)* Cousins, please let me travel with you and Jesus. Please say "yes."

JAMES:	*(Nods his head.)* Yes, Jeremiah! You may come with us!
JOHN:	Of course! We'd love to have you come with us, Jeremiah! And I know that Jesus will be very happy to see you.
JEREMIAH:	*(exuberantly)* Oh, thank you. Thank you both! *(ALL exit stage left.)*

Scene 2—Jerusalem

THADDEUS and JASON, stage left, are playing marbles. MIRIAM, ELIZABETH, JUDITH, stage center, are playing the dreidl game.

MIRIAM, JUDITH, ELIZABETH:	*(Sing the dreidl song as they spin.)* Dreidl, dreidl, dreidl I made it out of clay And when it's dry and ready A dreidl I will play.
JOSHUA:	*(Enters stage right and calls out to sisters at play:)* Miriam, Elizabeth, Judith . . . come here!
MIRIAM:	*(Stands and walks toward JOSHUA.)* What is it, Joshua? *(ELIZABETH and JUDITH join MIRIAM.)*
JOSHUA:	We're going to the fields now to gather branches.
ELIZABETH:	Why, Joshua?
JOSHUA:	There are many people coming to Jerusalem for Passover, Elizabeth. We're going to cover the roads with branches at the entrance to the city.
JUDITH:	We do it every year, Elizabeth. This year Mother said that you can come and help us.
ELIZABETH:	Oh, good! I'm glad I can help.
JOSHUA:	*(Takes a few steps and calls out to his brothers.)* Thaddeus, Jason, come, brothers! It's time to go!

(THADDEUS and JASON pick up their marbles.)

THADDEUS: *(Looks up at JOSHUA.)*
We're coming, Joshua.

JASON: *(Stands up.)*
Did you hear about the Rabbi who's coming, Joshua?

JOSHUA: What Rabbi?

JASON: The one that Daniel has been talking about!

MIRIAM: Our friend Daniel came by a little earlier and told us that a famous Rabbi would be entering the city very soon.

JOSHUA: *(thoughtfully)* Hmmm. Maybe it's Rabbi Jesus. He's the one who brought Jairus's daughter back to life. *(pause)* What else did Daniel say?

JUDITH: He told us that his Uncle Simon brought them some beautiful palm branches from Jericho.

ELIZABETH: And guess what, Joshua? Daniel said that he would give each of us a real palm branch to wave. Isn't that wonderful?

JOSHUA: That's very nice of Daniel, Elizabeth. Now, everyone, let's get down to the fields. The branches there have already been cut down. We need to gather them quickly and take them to the entrance of the city.

MIRIAM: I hope we get to see Jesus!

JUDITH: So do I!
(Following JOSHUA, they exit right.)

Scene 3—On the Road to Jerusalem

Four ISRAELITES enter stage left holding palm branches. They stop.

ISRAELITE 1: *(Places hand on forehead and looks toward stage right.)*
I think he's coming!

ISRAELITE 2: Can you see him?

ISRAELITE 1: *(Nods head excitedly.)*
Yes, I can see him. He's riding on a donkey.

ISRAELITE 3: *(Shakes head.)*
No, it's a young colt.

ISRAELITE 2: Are you sure it's Rabbi Jesus who's riding on a colt?

ISRAELITE 3: Yes!

ISRAELITE 4: Tell me, why is this Rabbi so special?

ISRAELITE 2: They say that he is the promised one. He will deliver us from the Romans.

ISRAELITE 1: Listen, everyone! I hear people shouting!

ISRAELITE 4: What are they saying?
(ISRAELITES 5 and 6 enter stage right.)

ISRAELITE 5: Hosanna! Blessed is the one who comes in the name of the Lord!

ISRAELITE 6: Blessed is the coming kingdom of our ancestor David! Hosanna in the highest heaven!

(JESUS enters the stage area holding the poster donkey sideways. He is surrounded by PETER, JAMES, JOHN, JEREMIAH, and several ISRAELITES waving palm branches. The entire group enters stage right, walks across the stage, and exits stage left while singing the song below.)

> **Hosanna in the Highest**
> Melody: A Tisket, A Tasket
>
> Hosanna! Hosanna!
> Hosanna in the highest!
> Oh, blessed is the one who comes.
> Hosanna in the highest!
>
> Hosanna! Hosanna!
> Hosanna in the highest!
> Oh, blessed is the one who comes.
> Hosanna in the highest!

(The song is repeated until everyone has left the stage.)

Scene 4—Jeremiah's Home in Jerusalem

MARTHA sits at a small table with her daughters ANN and LYDIA, who are standing and preparing the dip for Passover. Each one has a bowl and spoon and is busy at work. A bottle and three bowls are on the cloth spread out before them.

MARTHA: We've certainly made plenty of dip. I think this will be more than enough.

ANN: Mother, why do we eat the bitter herbs at the Passover meal?

MARTHA: The bitter herbs symbolize the bitterness of the slavery Moses and our ancestors experienced in Egypt.

LYDIA: Well, I'm glad that we can dip the herbs into this mixture of nuts and fruit. It makes the bitter herbs taste much better!

ANN: It sure does! May I try it now. Mother?

MARTHA: Yes, you may. I think we've put in the right amount of everything.

JEREMIAH: *(Enters stage right.)*
Mother, I'm home! Peace be to you, Mother! And to you, Lydia and Ann!

LYDIA: Peace be to you, Jeremiah!

ANN: Peace, Jeremiah!

MARTHA: Jeremiah, I'm so glad to see you.
(MARTHA stands up and hugs JEREMIAH.)
I was afraid you wouldn't be here for Passover.

JEREMIAH: Nothing could stop me from being in Jerusalem for Passover, Mother.

MARTHA: How are Sarah and her children?

JEREMIAH: Everyone is well, Mother. I have some exciting news to tell you.

ANN: *(eagerly)* What is it, Jeremiah?

JEREMIAH: I've been with James and John. We entered Jerusalem with Jesus.

LYDIA: Do you mean Rabbi Jesus? The one who made Jairus's daughter well?

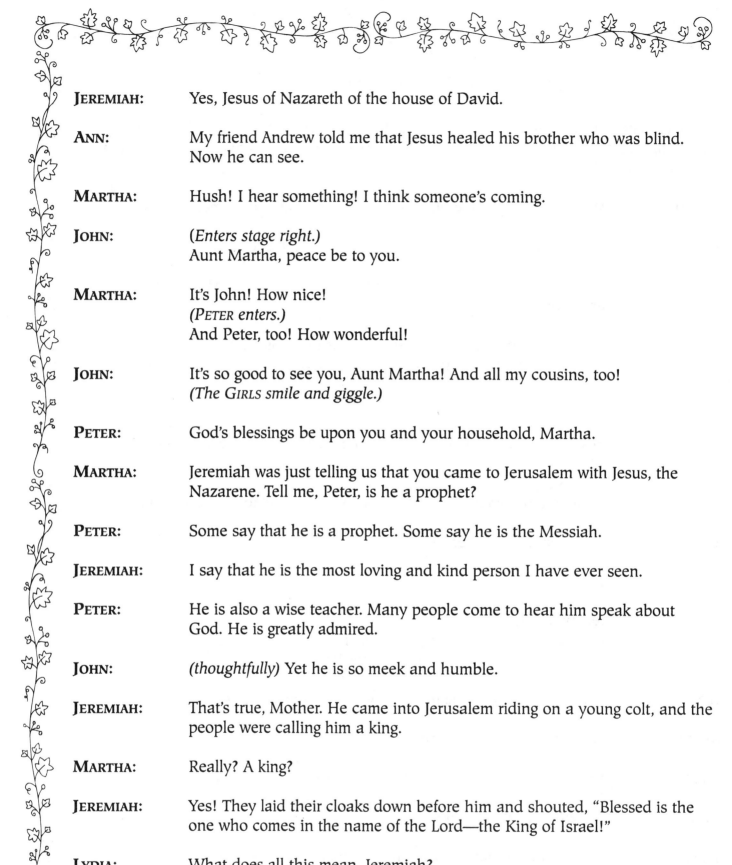

JEREMIAH: Yes, Jesus of Nazareth of the house of David.

ANN: My friend Andrew told me that Jesus healed his brother who was blind. Now he can see.

MARTHA: Hush! I hear something! I think someone's coming.

JOHN: (*Enters stage right.*)
Aunt Martha, peace be to you.

MARTHA: It's John! How nice!
(*PETER enters.*)
And Peter, too! How wonderful!

JOHN: It's so good to see you, Aunt Martha! And all my cousins, too!
(*The GIRLS smile and giggle.*)

PETER: God's blessings be upon you and your household, Martha.

MARTHA: Jeremiah was just telling us that you came to Jerusalem with Jesus, the Nazarene. Tell me, Peter, is he a prophet?

PETER: Some say that he is a prophet. Some say he is the Messiah.

JEREMIAH: I say that he is the most loving and kind person I have ever seen.

PETER: He is also a wise teacher. Many people come to hear him speak about God. He is greatly admired.

JOHN: (*thoughtfully*) Yet he is so meek and humble.

JEREMIAH: That's true, Mother. He came into Jerusalem riding on a young colt, and the people were calling him a king.

MARTHA: Really? A king?

JEREMIAH: Yes! They laid their cloaks down before him and shouted, "Blessed is the one who comes in the name of the Lord—the King of Israel!"

LYDIA: What does all this mean, Jeremiah?

JEREMIAH: I'm not sure, but I know that many people believe in him. They have seen his miracles.

JOHN:	We must leave now, dear cousin. *(He puts his arm around JEREMIAH.)*
PETER:	Yes, John and I must be on our way. We have preparations to make for the Passover meal.
MARTHA:	Do you have a place to go? You know that you are welcome here. We always have room for you.
JOHN:	Thank you, Aunt Martha, but we have a room in a house nearby.
PETER:	Yes, a man has graciously given us the use of his large upstairs room. It will do nicely for our teacher, Jesus, and the twelve of us, his disciples.
MARTHA:	The girls and I have just finished making dip for the bitter herbs. Please take some. We have plenty. *(LYDIA brings PETER a lid-covered bowl of dip.)*
PETER:	*(Takes the bowl.)* Thank you, Martha, and thank you, girls. Shalom! *(Bows head.)*
JOHN:	*(Bows head.)* Shalom, everyone! *(PETER and JOHN exit.)* *(MARTHA, JEREMIAH, LYDIA, and ANN pick up the spoons and bowls and exit.)*

Scene 5—Jeremiah's Home

JEREMIAH sleeps on a mat stage left. Nearby, there is a bench.
JOHN enters stage right. He sees JEREMIAH sleeping
and quietly walks to the bench and sits down. A rooster crows.

JEREMIAH:	*(Sits up.)* John, what are you doing here so early in the morning?
JOHN:	I know it's early, Jeremiah, but I've been awake for hours.
JEREMIAH:	What's the matter? Why couldn't you sleep? And where are your friends? *(A rooster crows again.)*

JOHN: I'm not sure where they are, Jeremiah. Everyone has scattered. They are confused and frightened!

JEREMIAH: Why? What's happened?
(A rooster crows for the third time.)

JOHN: Oh, Jeremiah! It's awful! They've taken Jesus. They've taken him away.

JEREMIAH: *(confused)* Taken Jesus? Who? Who's taken Jesus?

JOHN: The soldiers—the Roman soldiers. They arrested Jesus and took him away!

JEREMIAH: *(upset)* Why would they arrest Jesus? Tell me, John. What happened?

JOHN: *(JOHN stands up and walks to front stage.)*
It all happened after the Passover meal. Jesus wanted to pray. So, we went to our favorite place, the garden of Gethsemane. It was so peaceful, so quiet. Jesus asked Peter, James, and me to come with him to a special place in the garden to keep watch while he prayed. But *(pause)* we were so tired, Jeremiah, that we fell asleep.
(Lowers head in embarrassment.)

JEREMIAH: Then what happened?

JOHN: Jesus came and woke us up. He asked us to stay awake and pray.

JEREMIAH: Did you?

JOHN: We really tried, Jeremiah! But again we fell asleep, and once more he came and asked us to keep watch. When he came to us the third time, he said, "The hour has come. My betrayer is here." Then the soldiers came.

JEREMIAH: Betrayer? Did someone you know bring the soldiers to arrest Jesus?

JOHN: Yes. It was Judas Iscariot. *(tearfully)* I feel terrible. Why didn't I stay awake? I might have heard the soldiers coming and warned Jesus.

MARTHA: *(Enters stage left.)*
John! What's the matter? Why are you crying?

JEREMIAH: *(very upset)* Mother! The Roman soldiers have arrested Jesus. Judas betrayed him!

MARTHA: *(surprised)* Betrayed Jesus? Why?

JOHN: They took Jesus in for questioning, Martha. Some say that the religious leaders want to be rid of him.

MARTHA: Oh, my! How terrible! Where are the others?

JOHN: I don't know. Everyone was frightened and confused. I've been walking around for hours.

MARTHA: Come and lie down, John. You must rest. I'm going to awaken my husband. He'll know what to do. He'll speak to the elders.

JEREMIAH: Mother, I'll go to Joshua's house and ask his family if they know what's happened to Jesus.

MARTHA: Go, my son. I must speak to your father.
(Exits stage left.)

JEREMIAH: I'll come back as soon as I can, John. I'll find out about Jesus.

JOHN: Thank you, Jeremiah.

JEREMIAH: Don't worry, John. My father has friends in high places. I'm sure they will be able to do something to help Jesus.

JOHN: I hope so. God's blessing to you.
(JEREMIAH exits stage right. JOHN sits down on JEREMIAH's mat. He folds his hands in prayer and lifts his eyes to heaven.)
Our Father, who art in heaven, hallowed be thy name . . .
(His voice trails off.)

Scene 6—Morning in Jerusalem

JEREMIAH enters stage right. He stops and looks around for his friends.

JEREMIAH: *(Sees JASON entering stage left.)*
Jason! Jason!

JASON: *(Looks toward JEREMIAH.)*
Jeremiah!

JEREMIAH: *(Runs toward JASON.)*
Jason, have you heard any news about Jesus?

JASON: Yes, after the Sanhedrin questioned Jesus at Caiphas's house, they took him to the Praetorium.

JEREMIAH: Do you mean the Roman governor's palace?

JASON: Yes. The last thing I heard was that Pontius Pilate was questioning Jesus. *(Looks toward stage right. JOSHUA and THADDEUS enter.)*
Oh, look! I see Joshua and Thaddeus coming.

JEREMIAH: Joshua! What did you find out?

THADDEUS: I'm afraid it's not good, Jeremiah!

JEREMIAH: Tell me. I have to know!

JOSHUA: The soldiers brought Jesus to the judgment seat outside the palace where a large crowd had gathered. Pilate said that he would release a prisoner to them because it was Passover.

JASON: So, did Pilate release Jesus?

JOSHUA: Well, he asked the people if they wanted him to release Jesus or another prisoner, Barabbas, a murderer.

JEREMIAH: I'm sure that they picked Jesus.

JOSHUA: No, Jeremiah. They didn't. They picked Barabbas.

JEREMIAH: They couldn't have!

JASON: Then what did they do with Jesus?

THADDEUS: The people screamed, "Crucify him!"

JEREMIAH: *(Shakes his head in disbelief.)*
No! No! They wouldn't want him crucified. They love him.

JOSHUA: *(softly)* I'm afraid it's true, Jeremiah. Pilate asked the people what they wanted him to do with Jesus and they shouted, "Crucify him."

JEREMIAH: *(Paces back and forth.)*
I have to go! There must be a way to stop this! I'll find my father. He'll know what to do.

Scene 7—Outside Jeremiah's House

BENJAMIN sits on a bench, plucking a stringed instrument.

JEREMIAH: *(Runs in from stage left.)*
Father! Father!

BENJAMIN: *(Stands up quickly.)*
Jeremiah!

JEREMIAH: *(surprised)* Benjamin! What are you doing at *my* house?

BENJAMIN: I came to see you! We're staying at my uncle's during Passover. Do you know about your friend, Jesus?

JEREMIAH: I know that they're talking about crucifying him! Can you believe that, Benjamin? Jesus who has made the blind see, the deaf hear, and the lame walk. Why would they want to crucify him? He's been so good to them!

BENJAMIN: I'm sorry, Jeremiah.

JEREMIAH: I must talk to my father! He'll do something.

BENJAMIN: Your father has already gone. But it's too late! No one can do anything now.

JEREMIAH: What do you mean?

BENJAMIN: My uncle just came back from the road that leads to Calvary. He saw Jesus *(pause)* . . . he saw Jesus carrying the cross for his crucifixion.

JEREMIAH: No, no, no!
(Sits down on the bench and hangs his head.)

(BENJAMIN walks over to JEREMIAH and puts his hand on his shoulder. JEREMIAH stands and walks with BENJAMIN into his house, exit right.)

ISRAELITES: *(Enter stage left singing.)*

Were You There? (traditional)
Were you there when they crucified my Lord?
Were you there when they crucified my Lord?
Oh, sometimes it causes me to tremble, tremble, tremble.
Were you there when they crucified my Lord?

Were you there when they nailed him to the tree?
Were you there when they nailed him to the tree?
Oh, sometimes it causes me to tremble, tremble, tremble.
Were you there when they nailed him to the tree?

Were you there when they laid him in the tomb?
Were you there when they laid him in the tomb?
Oh, sometimes it causes me to tremble, tremble, tremble.
Were you there when they laid him in the tomb?

(ISRAELITES, with heads bowed down, quietly exit stage left.)

Scene 8—*Early Sunday Morning Inside Jeremiah's House*

JEREMIAH and BENJAMIN sleep on mats covered by sheets.

JEREMIAH:	*(Sits up at BENJAMIN's side and whispers loudly.)* Benjamin, wake up! *(pause)* Wake up, Benjamin!
BENJAMIN:	*(Sits up.)* What is it, Jeremiah?
JEREMIAH:	*(pleadingly)* Benjamin, please come with me.
BENJAMIN:	Where? Where are you going, Jeremiah?
JEREMIAH:	I'm going to the tomb.
BENJAMIN:	The tomb?
JEREMIAH:	Yes, I want to see where they put Jesus. Today is Sunday. It's been *two* days already. I *must* go today.
BENJAMIN:	*(hesitantly)* I'm not sure that we should go there.

JEREMIAH:	*(earnestly)* I have to go there. I . . .
BENJAMIN:	*(Shakes his head.)* You don't have to explain, Jeremiah. I understand. I'll go with you.

Scene 9—On the Road to the Tomb

PETER enters stage left. JOHN follows.

PETER:	*(Talks to himself as he walks toward stage right.)* Where could they have taken Jesus' body?
JOHN:	Who, Peter? Who do you think took Jesus' body?
PETER:	I don't know. Tell me, John. Who could have moved such a heavy stone?
JOHN:	It would have taken several men.
PETER:	And what about the strips of linen in which his body was wrapped? *(Stops and turns to JOHN.)* John, did you notice the wrappings?
JOHN:	*(Looks quizzically at PETER.)* What about them, Peter?
PETER:	*(strongly)* All of the wrappings are still in the tomb! *(Slight pause, thoughtfully.)* And another thing, they were lying there so neatly. How strange!
JOHN:	Do you think that it was the Roman soldiers?
PETER:	I'm not sure. Come, let's walk. *(Both walk toward stage right.)* *(JEREMIAH and BENJAMIN enter stage right.)*
JOHN:	*(Sees JEREMIAH.)* Jeremiah! What are you doing here?
JEREMIAH:	Benjamin and I are going to the tomb. I want to see where they laid Jesus.

JOHN:	He's not there, Jeremiah!
JEREMIAH:	He's not? Where is he?
PETER:	We don't know. His body is gone!
BENJAMIN:	Gone? Did you say his body is gone?
JOHN:	The tomb is empty!
JEREMIAH:	*(puzzled)* I don't understand. I have to see for myself. *(JEREMIAH runs ahead and exits.)*
BENJAMIN:	*(shouts)* Wait, Jeremiah! I'm coming! *(BENJAMIN runs after JEREMIAH and exits.)*
PETER:	Come, John! Let's go tell the apostles! *(PETER and JOHN quickly exit stage left.)*

Scene 10—Near the Tomb

MARY MAGDALENE enters from the right.

MARY:	*(Stops and clasps her hands together.)* Praise be to God! Praise be his holy name!

(BENJAMIN and JEREMIAH enter stage left.)

BENJAMIN:	*(Sees MARY and calls out.)* Mary! Mary Magdalene!
JEREMIAH:	*(Quickly walks to MARY.)* Mary, do you know where we can find Jesus?
MARY:	*(excitedly)* I've just seen him! I've seen my Lord!
BENJAMIN:	Where, Mary? Where is he?
MARY:	He's alive! HE IS ALIVE!
JEREMIAH:	*(puzzled)* Alive? How can he be alive?

BENJAMIN:	Mary, they've crucified Jesus. *(pause)* You know that he died on the cross.
MARY:	I tell you that he's alive. I have seen him! He has risen from the dead.
JEREMIAH:	*(excitedly)* Did you hear that, Benjamin? Mary has seen Jesus. He's alive!
BENJAMIN:	*(stammering)* I . . . I don't know what to say!
MARY:	Jesus told me to go to the disciples. I must tell them the good news! *(MARY exits stage left.)*
JEREMIAH:	I'm going home to tell my family! I'm so happy!
BENJAMIN:	And I must tell my uncle! *(JEREMIAH and BENJAMIN quickly exit stage left.)*

(JEREMIAH, BENJAMIN, PETER, JAMES, JOHN, and MARY MAGDALENE return to the stage area singing the opening line of "Jesus Christ Is Risen Today." The ENTIRE CAST joins them on stage to sing the rest of the song.)

JEREMIAH AND OTHERS:

    (sing)   Jesus Christ is ris'n today, Alleluia!

ALL:

    (sing)   Our triumphant holy day, Alleluia!
Who did once upon the cross, Alleluia!
Suffer to redeem our loss, Alleluia!

Hymns of praise then let us sing, Alleluia!
Unto Christ, our heav'nly King, Alleluia!
Who endured the cross and grave, Alleluia!
Sinners to redeem and save, Alleluia!

Jesus and the Children

Characters

Jasmine, young girl

Brendan, Jasmine's younger brother
Mother, of Jasmine and Brendan
Amy, newcomer to Vacation Bible School
Devin, Amy's younger brother
Erica, VBS classmate
Spencer, VBS classmate
Angelica, angel
Jesus
Peter, Jesus' disciple
James, Jesus' disciple
Rachel, a young girl
Esther, Rachel's mother
Andrew, a friend of Rachel
3 men listening to Jesus
3–4 mothers with 6–8 children to see Jesus

Costumes

present-day clothing (Scene 1); nightgown, tunic to wear over gown (Scenes 2–5)
pajamas
modern-day clothing
modern-day clothing
modern-day clothing
modern-day clothing
modern-day clothing
white gown
simple robe and tunic
simple robe and tunic
simple robe and tunic
simple tunic
simple robe and tunic
simple tunic
simple robes and tunics
simple tunics

Props

child's bicycle
2 mattresses with a pillow and blanket for each
low nightstand or milk-carton carrier covered with cloth
lamp
silk flowers and basket
fake rock

Setting

Keep the setting simple so that the prop people can change scenes quickly. A light blue cloth, curtain, or sheet with four pieces of Velcro attached can serve as the backdrop for the outdoor and indoor scenes.

For Scenes 1, 3 and 4: attach two white paper clouds to the Velcro to symbolize the sky. In Scene 1, place a modern-day bench and a child's bicycle on the stage to indicate the current year. In Scene 4, a fake rock for Jesus to sit on is needed. For Scenes 2 and 5: prop people will remove the clouds on the blue backdrop and attach two religious posters or pictures of angels. This will be the wall in the children's bedroom. The lightweight foam mattresses, pillows, and quilts below the posters will further add to the bedroom scene. Place the nightstand and lamp between the two beds.

Scene 1—Warm Summer Morning

Children are leaving Vacation Bible School and heading home.

AMY, ERICA, SPENCER, BRENDAN, AND DEVIN:
(Enter from stage left singing.)
Jesus loves me, this I know,
For the Bible tells me so.

JASMINE:
(Enters stage left and interrupts the children's singing.)
Hey, everyone. Wait for me! I'm coming!
(She looks back.)
Good-bye, Mrs. Smith! See you tomorrow!
(She runs to her friends, who have stopped to wait for her.)

BRENDAN: Did you find your bracelet, Jasmine?

JASMINE: *(Shows the bracelet.)*
Mrs. Smith found it. I'm glad she's our teacher. She's really nice.

AMY: She sure is. And I like the Bible songs that she's been teaching us.

DEVIN: So do I!

SPENCER: I like the way she makes the stories from the Bible sound so exciting!

ERICA: And so real! I love the story she told us about Jesus and the children.

JASMINE: I do too. *(longingly)* I wish that I could have been there to sit on Jesus' lap.

ERICA: And listen to him tell stories!

SPENCER: I'd like to have been in the boat with Jesus and the disciples when that big storm came while they were on the lake.

DEVIN: What happened?

SPENCER: The storm got worse and worse. The boat began filling up with water.

JASMINE: The disciples were really afraid!

ERICA: They thought that they would drown.

JASMINE: But Jesus told them not to be afraid.

SPENCER: *(dramatically)* He told the sea, "Be still!"

ERICA: *(with awe)* And the sea became still!

BRENDAN: I like that story.

AMY: There are lots of awesome stories about Jesus in the Bible.

SPENCER: Yes! True stories about all the wonderful things that Jesus did for people.

ERICA: He still does wonderful things!

JASMINE: That's because Jesus loves everyone!

AMY: I wonder which story Mrs. Smith will tell us tomorrow.

DEVIN: I hope it's the story about Peter not catching any fish.

BRENDAN: Why, Devin? Does it remind you of when you and your dad go fishing?
(Everyone, including DEVIN, laughs lightheartedly.)

DEVIN: We'll catch a big fish one of these days! We'll catch a whole string of 'em!

AMY: I hope not, Devin! Then we'll have to eat them!

DEVIN: MMMMmmmm! Yum, yum!

AMY: Yuck! You and Dad can eat them all. Mom and I will have pizza!
(ERICA, SPENCER, JASMINE, and BRENDAN chuckle.)
Well, good-bye everyone! Devin and I turn here.

DEVIN: *(Looks at AMY.)*
I almost forgot! We're going to Grandma's house today!
(Turns to his friends.)
Bye, everyone!

ERICA: *(Waves.)*
Good-bye! See you tomorrow!

DEVIN: See you tomorrow!
(AMY and DEVIN walk toward the back of stage right and exit.)

JASMINE:	What's your favorite song from Vacation Bible School, Erica?
ERICA:	*(Begins singing.)* He's got the whole world in his hands.
JASMINE:	*(Joins ERICA in singing the second line.)* He's got the whole world in his hands. *(ERICA and JASMINE walk toward front stage right and exit.)*
SPENCER AND BRENDAN:	*(Follow behind the girls, singing.)* He's got the whole world in his hands He's got the whole world in his hands. *(SPENCER and BRENDAN exit front stage right.)*

Scene 2—That Night in the Children's Bedroom

MOTHER:	*(Enters.)* Well, children! Have you said your prayers?
JASMINE:	I have, Mother!
BRENDAN:	Me, too!
MOTHER:	*(Pulls the covers up on JASMINE.)* Good! Now get to sleep . . . both of you! *(Pulls the covers up on BRENDAN.)* You'll be going to Vacation Bible School early in the morning.
BRENDAN:	Oh, good! I had so much fun today.
MOTHER:	I'm glad you did! What did you do that was the most fun?
BRENDAN:	We played a game called "Daniel's in the Lions' Den"!
JASMINE:	In our class, Mrs. Smith told us a great story about Jesus.
MOTHER:	Well, tomorrow will be another exciting day! Sweet dreams, children. Remember, God loves you and I do too!
JASMINE:	Good night, Mother!
BRENDAN:	Good night, Mother!

MOTHER:	Good night, children! *(Turns off the lamp. Silence for thirty seconds.)*
JASMINE:	*(Whispers loudly.)* Brendan! *(pause)* Brendan, are you sleeping?
BRENDAN:	*(sleepily)* Uh-huh.
JASMINE:	I'd have loved to be there when Jesus told the disciples to let the children come to him. Wouldn't you, Brendan? *(pause)* Brendan? I guess he's sleeping. I know . . . I'll talk to God! God always listens. *(Folds her hands.)* Dear God, it's me, Jasmine. I don't mean to bug you, but I'm here to ask you again. *(yawns)* God, please can I go back in time to Galilee to see Jesus? I want to hear him tell stories. *(yawns)* It would be so special if I could . . . *(Her head drops, and she closes her eyes briefly.)* Where was I? Oh, yes! I was talking to God. *(She hears the tinkling sound of chimes.)* What's that sound? Who's there?
ANGELICA:	*(Enters the room.)* It is I, Angelica.
JASMINE:	Who are you?
ANGELICA:	I'm an angel. God has sent me to take you back in time.
JASMINE:	Oh, my! Really? Is this really happening?
ANGELICA:	Yes, this is really happening. I have brought you a simple garment to wear so that you will be dressed like the children of Galilee.
JASMINE:	I'm so excited! Oh, thank you, God. *(With ANGELICA's help, she puts the tunic on over her nightgown.)*
ANGELICA:	Here is a sash to tie around your waist. *(ANGELICA ties a sash around JASMINE's waist.)*
JASMINE:	This is great!
ANGELICA:	Come, Jasmine, let's go! *(ANGELICA takes JASMINE's hand and they exit.)*

Scene 3—Galilee

RACHEL sits on a cloth at the side of a road arranging flowers in a small basket.

RACHEL: *(Sings to herself.)*
La-la-la-la-la-la-la. La-la-la . . .
(ANGELICA and JASMINE enter stage right and walk toward RACHEL.)

RACHEL: *(Looks up at ANGELICA and JASMINE.)* La-la-la . . . Oh! I didn't see you coming. Peace be to you! I'm Rachel.
(She looks at JASMINE.)
Who are you?

JASMINE: I'm Jasmine and this is my friend, Angelica!

RACHEL: Jasmine. What a pretty name! I've never heard it before! Are you from Galilee?

ANGELICA: No, we're from far away. We've just arrived in Galilee.

RACHEL: Did you come to see Jesus?

JASMINE AND ANGELICA:
Yes, we did!
(They smile at each other.)

RACHEL: So many people have been coming! My mother and I were there when Jesus fed a crowd of thousands.

JASMINE: Tell us about it.

ANGELICA: Yes, please do.
(JASMINE and ANGELICA sit down on the ground.)

RACHEL: Well, a large crowd of people were listening to Jesus talk for a long time. It was getting late, and we were getting hungry.

ANDREW: *(Enters.)*
Rachel!

RACHEL: Shalom, Andrew. This is Jasmine and Angelica. Tell them what Jesus did with your barley loaves and fish.

ANDREW:	It was miraculous! I gave his disciples two barley loaves and five fish. Jesus blessed the food and asked the disciples to give it to the people.
RACHEL:	And they did! The disciples gave the food to all of us. We kept eating until we were full!
ANDREW:	There was enough for everyone! For thousands of people.
RACHEL:	They even had leftovers. Baskets of leftovers!
JASMINE:	That's amazing!
ANGELICA:	Jesus multiplied the loaves and fishes because he wanted to feed everyone.
JASMINE:	Jesus loves everyone, doesn't he, Angelica?
ANGELICA:	Yes, he truly does.
JASMINE:	Andrew, where is Jesus now?
ANDREW:	We heard that he's coming to a place near here.
RACHEL:	Andrew and I are going with my mother to see him. Would the two of you like to join us?
JASMINE:	Oh, yes! Thank you.
ANGELICA:	Thank you very much.
RACHEL:	Come now. Mother is waiting. *(ALL exit.)*

Scene 4—On a Hillside in Galilee

JESUS sits on a large rock talking to some men. Several children and their mothers sit nearby. PETER and JAMES stand next to JESUS.

ESTHER:	*(Enters followed by RACHEL, ANDREW, JASMINE, and ANGELICA.)* Hurry, children! I see Jesus!
RACHEL:	*(Points to JESUS.)* There he is, Jasmine.

JASMINE: Oh, Rachel. I'm so excited.
(Turns to ANGELICA.)
Angelica, I can hardly believe this is happening.
(ANGELICA smiles.)

ESTHER: Children, come! I will ask Jesus to bless you.
(ESTHER walks up to JESUS with RACHEL and ANDREW. PETER and JAMES step forward.)

JAMES: *(Strongly to ESTHER.)* Please, do not bring the children here. Jesus is busy.

PETER: *(Gently but firmly to the CHILDREN.)* Jesus is talking to some men. Don't interrupt him.

JESUS: Peter! James! Do not stop the children. Let them come to me.
(To the CHILDREN.) Come, children. I will pray for God's blessing on you.
(PETER and JAMES bring RACHEL and ANDREW to JESUS.)

Father, I ask your blessing on these, your little ones. Protect them from evil and lead them to your heavenly kingdom.
(JESUS puts one hand on each child's head.)
God be with you, children.

RACHEL AND ANDREW:
Thank you, Jesus.
(They return with ESTHER to the crowd.)

JESUS: *(Looks at JASMINE.)*
Jasmine, come here to me. I want to see you.

JASMINE: Angelica! Jesus is calling me! He knows my name!

ANGELICA: Yes, Jasmine. He wants you to come to him.

JASMINE: I'm coming, Jesus.

JESUS: Come closer to me, Jasmine.
(JESUS puts his arms around JASMINE. He looks into her eyes.)
Jasmine, you are special. There is no one just like you. I love you very much.

JASMINE: I love you, Jesus. You are so good to me and to everyone. I just had to come and tell you, "Thank you." Thank you for loving us so much.

JESUS: Never forget that I will always love you.
(JESUS puts his hand on JASMINE's head.)
God's blessings upon you, Jasmine. Please tell everyone you see that I love them very much.
(JESUS stands and starts walking through the crowd.)

ESTHER: Look! Jesus is coming!

JESUS: God's blessings upon you. Go in peace. *(Puts his hand on individual heads as he walks toward stage left. The crowd follows him. ALL exit.)*

Scene 5—Jasmine and Brendan's Bedroom

ANGELICA and JASMINE are returning home from Galilee.
BRENDAN is asleep in his bed.

JASMINE: Angelica, this is the greatest thing that has ever happened to me.

ANGELICA: I'm glad that you're so happy, Jasmine!

JASMINE: Jesus told me that he loves me very much.

ANGELICA: He really does, Jasmine.

JASMINE: And he loves everyone very much, every person in the world!

ANGELICA: That's because he is all-loving.

JASMINE: I'm so happy. I feel like I'm floating on a cloud.

ANGELICA: Now, let's take off your sash and your robe. It's time for you to get in bed.
(Helps JASMINE take off these items.)

JASMINE: *(Climbs into bed.)*
Angelica, tell God thank you for me.

ANGELICA: You can tell him, Jasmine. God is always listening. Sweet dreams!

JASMINE: Good night, Angelica.
(ANGELICA walks out carrying the robe. The sash is left behind.)

MOTHER: *(Enters stage left.)*
Jasmine! Brendan! It's time to get up for Vacation Bible School.

BRENDAN: Can we have pancakes for breakfast, Mother?

MOTHER: Sure. *(pause)* Jasmine, it's time to get out of bed.

JASMINE: Yes, Mother! I'm getting up.

MOTHER: Get ready, and I'll go downstairs and cook pancakes.

JASMINE: Thank you, Mother.
(MOTHER exits. JASMINE gets out of bed and walks over to BRENDAN.)

JASMINE: Brendan, did you see an angel in our room last night?

BRENDAN: What? What did you say?

JASMINE: I want to know if you saw an angel in our room.

BRENDAN: *(Shakes head.)*
No, Jasmine. There was no angel here.

JASMINE: There *was* an angel here, Brendan. Her name was Angelica. She took me to see Jesus in Galilee.

BRENDAN: Jasmine, you must have been dreaming!

JASMINE: No! It wasn't a dream. I really did see Jesus. He told me to tell you that he loves you very much.

BRENDAN: I know Jesus loves me, Jasmine. But I still think that you were dreaming. I'm going downstairs to eat pancakes. Are you coming?

JASMINE: In a minute.
(BRENDAN exits quickly.)
I can't believe it was a dream. It couldn't have been. It all seemed so real.

MOTHER: *(Calls loudly.)* Jasmine, breakfast is ready. Come and eat it while it's hot!

JASMINE: I'm coming, Mother!
                (Sees the sash.)
                What's this?
                (Picks up the sash.)
                This looks like the sash I wore in Galilee.
                (Rubs the sash on the side of her face.)
                Now I know it wasn't a dream. I can still see Jesus smiling at me.
                (sings)

                Jesus loves me, yes I know
                He's the one that told me so
                He loves everyone, it's true
                He loves me and he loves you

                (exits, singing)
                Yes, Jesus loves me
                Yes, Jesus loves me
                Yes, Jesus loves me
                He has told me so.

ALL CHARACTERS:
                (Come back on stage singing.)
                Jesus loves me, this I know,
                For the Bible tells me so.
                Little ones to him belong.
                We are weak but he is strong.

ANGELICA: *(to the audience)* Everyone, please join us.

EVERYONE:
                (sing)   Yes, Jesus loves me
                Yes, Jesus loves me
                Yes, Jesus loves me
                The Bible tells me so.

The Disciples Go Fishing

Readers: *Two groups*
Setting: *Group A stands on the left side.*
Group B stands on the right side.
Action: *Group A begins and Group B echoes each line.*

Group A	**Group B**
Let's go fishing.	Let's go fishing.
Let's catch some fish.	Let's catch some fish.
Hundreds of big fish.	Hundreds of big fish.
Hundreds of little fish.	Hundreds of little fish.
All right!	All right!
Let's go!	Let's go!

(Together, both groups now slap thighs to make a walking sound.)

Group A	**Group B**
Get in the boat now.	Get in the boat now.
Come sit down.	Come sit down.
Don't tip it over.	Don't tip it over.
Don't move around.	Don't move around.
All right!	All right!
Sit down!	Sit down!
(Clap hands once; sit down.)	*(Clap hands once; sit down.)*

Group A	**Group B**
Pick up the net.	Pick up the net.
Throw it in the sea.	Throw it in the sea.
Drop it down.	Drop it down.
So very deep.	So very deep.
All right!	All right!
Drop it deep.	Drop it deep.
(Strike floor with fists.)	*(Strike floor with fists.)*

Group A	**Group B**
Pull up the net	Pull up the net
Out of the sea.	Out of the sea.
See what's there.	See what's there.
Not a thing.	Not a thing.
All right!	All right!
It's empty.	It's empty.
(Show empty palms.)	*(Show empty palms.)*

Group A	**Group B**
Let's try the other side.	Let's try the other side.
Pick up the net.	Pick up the net.
Throw it in the sea.	Throw it in the sea.
Drop it down.	Drop it down.
So very deep.	So very deep.
All right!	All right!
Drop it deep.	Drop it deep.

(Together, both groups now strike the floor loudly with their fists.)

Group A	**Group B**
Pull up the net	Pull up the net
Out of the sea.	Out of the sea.
See what's there.	See what's there.
Not a thing.	Not a thing.
All right!	All right!
No fish. *(Show empty palms.)*	No fish. *(Show empty palms.)*
Time to go.	Time to go.

Group A	**Group B**
We see Jesus.	We see Jesus.
On the shore.	On the shore.
He calls out,	He calls out,
"Try once more."	"Try once more."
All right!	All right!
Once more. *(Hold up index finger.)*	Once more. *(Hold up index finger.)*

Group A	Group B
Pick up the net.	Pick up the net.
Throw it in the sea.	Throw it in the sea.
Drop it down	Drop it down
So very deep.	So very deep.
All right!	All right!
Drop it deep.	Drop it deep.

(Together, both groups now strike the floor loudly with their fists.)

Group A	Group B
Pull up the net	Pull up the net
Out of the sea.	Out of the sea.
See what's there.	See what's there.
It's full as can be.	It's full as can be.
All right!	All right!
Yes, siree!	Yes, siree!

Group A	Group B
We went fishing.	We went fishing.
No fish there.	No fish there.
Jesus came.	Jesus came.
Thousands ev'rywhere.	Thousands ev'rywhere.
All right!	All right!
Amen.	Amen.

Zacchaeus Finds God

Characters
READER 1, a solo reader
GROUP A, a number of readers speaking in unison
READER 2, another solo reader
GROUP B, a second group of readers speaking in unison

READER 1 stands in front of GROUP A on the left side of the stage area.
READER 2 stands in front of GROUP B on the right side of the stage area.

READERS 1 AND 2:
    (together) This is the story of Zacchaeus.

READER 1:   Zacchaeus was a little man who wanted to see Jesus.

GROUP A: He wasn't tall.
    He was very small.

READER 2:   One day Zacchaeus heard that Jesus was coming to Jericho.

GROUP B: He heard them say
    He was coming that day.

READER 1:   Zacchaeus decided to go where Jesus would be.

GROUP A: Decided to go
    to Jericho.

READER 2:   As Zacchaeus came near the place where Jesus was walking, he saw crowds of people.

GROUP B: People were there
    from everywhere.

READER 1:   Zacchaeus tried to push his way through the crowd.

GROUP A: He tried to get through.
    It was too hard to do.

READER 2:   Zacchaeus was determined to find another way to see Jesus.

GROUP B:	He looked around. No way could be found.
READER 1:	Finally, Zacchaeus climbed a sycamore tree along the path.
GROUP A:	He climbed a tree Lord Jesus to see.
READER 2:	When Jesus came to the sycamore tree, he called to Zacchaeus:
GROUP B:	"Climb down the tree. You're special to me."
READER 1:	Jesus told Zacchaeus to hurry because he was going to his house.
GROUP A:	"Come, keep up the pace. Let's hurry to your place."
READER 2:	Zacchaeus welcomed Jesus gladly.
GROUP B:	"Follow me. My guest you'll be."
READER 1:	Zacchaeus felt nine feet tall that day.
GROUP A:	"I'm a little man, But I feel so grand."
READER 2:	Zacchaeus told Jesus, "Lord, here and now, I give half of my possessions to the poor, and if I have cheated anybody, I will pay them back four times the amount.
GROUP B:	"I'll give half to the poor. To the others, I'll pay more!"
GROUP A:	He has repented.
GROUP B:	He has been saved.
GROUP A:	Alleluia! Alleluia!
GROUP B:	Amen. Amen.